VISIT US AT
www.abdopub.com

Spotlight, a division of ABDO Publishing Company Inc., is the school and library distributor of the Marvel Entertainment books.

Library bound edition © 2006

Library of Congress Cataloging-in-Publication Data

Vacation of Doom!

ISBN 1-59961-035-3   (Reinforced Library Bound Edition)

Gr. Novel.

Soon...

--and *now* we're not going to reach the *campsite* until *well after dark.*

Your *Dad* and I put a *lot of time* into planning *this trip* and--

We're *really* sorry, Mom. Something... *came up...*

Then *blew up!*

Jack!

Well, *hello,* Dolly!

How about a *hot date* with the *world's greatest hero*--

--the *Human Torch?*

Dolly *isn't* interested, Jack. She's *focused* on a *career.*

Plus, *boys are icky.*

I'll show you *"icky"...*

EWWW!

Daaaad! Jack's all gassy!

I *told* you to *go before we left,* Jack!

Later that night...

Well, last time I *checked*, *Medieval Times* ain't guarded by *laser-blasting super-robots!*

"Kooky theme restaurant," eh?

Just *think* what the *others* are gonna say when they find out I was *right!*

You're so much *smarter* than us, Jack!

We never should have *doubted* you!

I'm a *stoopid baby!*

Really...? You want *me* to be the *leader?!*

Well, it's *about--*

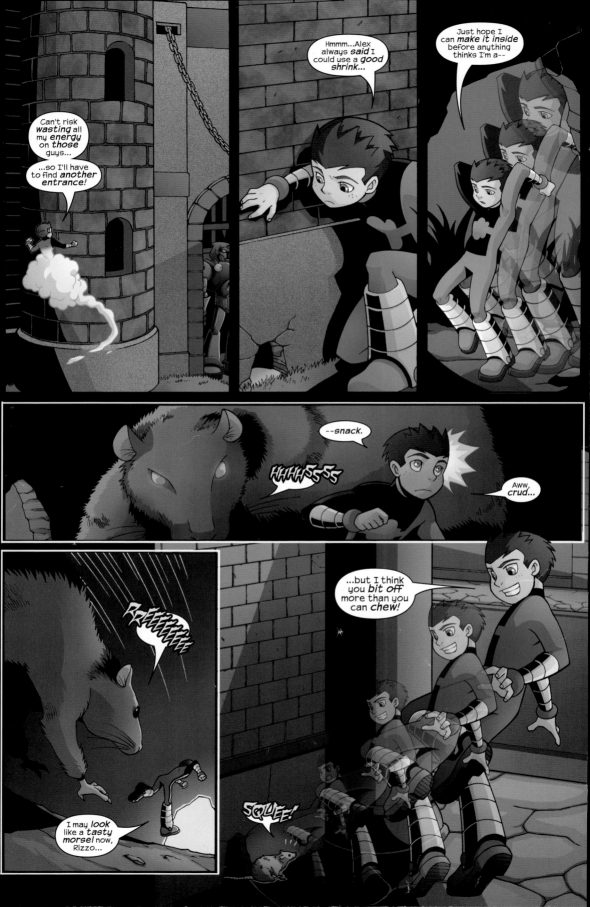

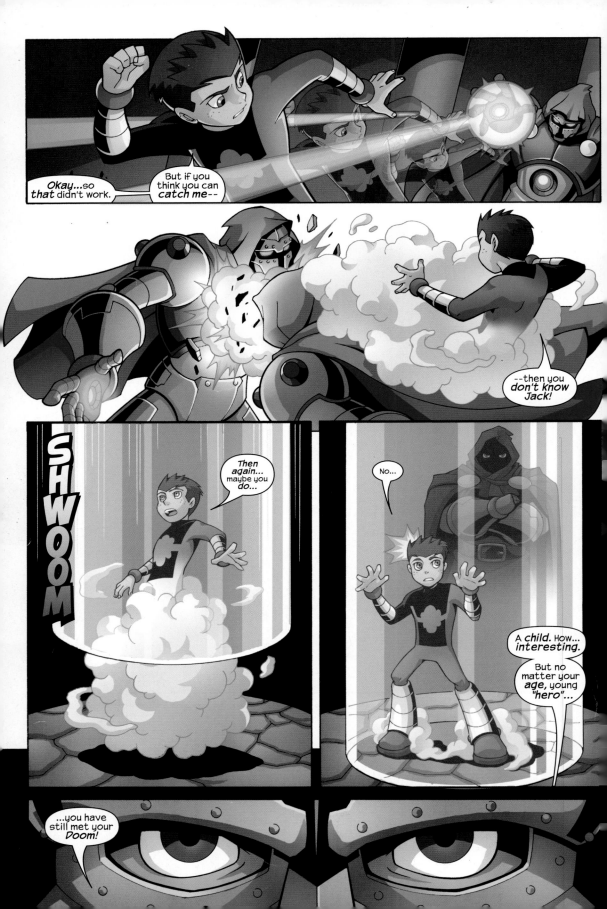

The question **is**, what are **you** doing here?

I saw the **flare** and wanted to **help**. You?

The **Fantastic Four** got a **call** about a busted **Doombot** in a nearby **town**.

It looked like it had been on a **supply run** for **his royal ugliness**, so we knew Doom was--

The robot?! We **destroyed** that!

My brother and sis...umm...my **teammates** and I!

And where are **they** now?

They...they **don't know** I came here.

Sounds like we've got a **lot in common**, kid.

Reed--Mr. Fantastic--he wanted to plan some **big strategy** to take down Doom.

Me? I jumped the gun and came here **on my own**.

And look where **that** landed me...

...I guess that's what I **get** for always trying to be the **superstar**, eh?

Yeah... I **guess** so...

Are you *sure* about this, Alex?

I mean, maybe Jack just went *into the woods* to...*you know*...

Yeah...what makes you *think* he would *come here?*

The fact that I specifically *told him* not to.

So, what do you think we're *up against?*

From the *look* of it, the same type of *robot* as *before*... plus a *friend.*

We *barely* beat *that one.* How are we gonna take down *two of them?*

We're *not.*

If *Jack* is *in there* we've gotta go *straight* to the *heart* of the--

--oh boy.

You now...

...two of them are looking *pretty good* right now...

They're *not* attacking!

But whatever *that thing* is, it's *turning on!*

Well, well...you're not at all the *house-guests* Doom was *expecting.*

And *unfortunately for you,* Doctor Doom has wasted *far* too much time on *children playing hero* for one night.

You *better not* have *hurt* my *brother,* Doctor *Dumb!*

Such *fire* from one so *young!*

A *shame* that it must now be *extinguished...*

That doesn't sound good.

Doesn't look good either!

Thing: Over already?! Well, howsabout that! You *kids* ain't so *bad!*

Invisible Woman: It's not over *quite yet,* Thing. We still need to help Reed find *Johnny* and--

Mr. Fantastic: One step *ahead* of you, dear!

Johnny: Hey, sis...

Invisible Woman: Jack! We were so *worried!*

Jack: About *me?* Come *on!*

When I heard that *you guys* were in *trouble,* I *called in* some--

Mr. Fantastic: *The truth,* young man?

Jack: Okay...sorry, Mr. Fantastic.

Jack: *Truth is,* you guys *saved my butt.* I screwed up. *Bad.*

Johnny: We *both* did. But now I think we *realize* how *important* it is to *count on* the rest of our *teams* to back us up.

The End.